What a Catch!

Sharon Gordon
Illustrated by Joe Boddy

RIGBY

Sam and her dad went fishing.

Dad sat down and Sam fished.

"Have you got a fish?"
asked Dad.
"No," said Sam. "I've got a frog."

"Have you got a fish?"
asked Dad.
"No," said Sam. "I've got a turtle

"Have you got a fish yet?"
asked Dad.
"No," said Sam. "I've got a snake

Just then, Sam felt a big tug.

"Yikes!" yelled Dad.

"What have you got?"

13

"I've got a big fish!" yelled Sam.
"What a catch!" said Dad.

"I'm going to let it go,"
said Sam. "Goodbye, fish!"